THE RICHEST MAN IN THE HOSPITAL

by Dr. Chris Condon

Edited by Lil Barcaski

Published by: GWN Publishing
www.GWNPublishing.com

Cover Design: Kristina Conatser Captured by KC Design

ISBN: 978-1-959608-60-8

DEDICATION

To varying degrees, this book has been in the works for the last couple of years. The ideas to share and how to bring them to relevance in one's daily life and personal health care have finally come to light with the encouragement of my wife, Allyson. We've celebrated life together now for thirty years and have been best friends since we met. She has been there with me, all along, through the challenges of being apart while I was away in school, and then building our lives and raising a family all while serving hundreds of patients every week for two decades.

Ally, you're my every day, my all the time, the love of my life and the inspiration for all I do.

I would also like to thank so many friends that have encouraged me to write and most recently a great friend, coach and mentor, Julie Jones. I recognize how God puts certain people in our path at the right time. Julie has been one of those people who has shared her own insights and beliefs and has been a great source of energy and light helping me see the need to share my ideas and to have the courage to write this book.

Finally, I write this book for all those who have lost faith and direction in their lives and who need to believe more in themselves and self-worth. You are enough. You deserve to live a life of abundance—including a life of great health!

TABLE OF CONTENTS

"In a world where over ten thousand books are published daily, it may seem unnecessary to add another to the mix. However, Dr. Condon's book fills a crucial need by simplifying the complex pursuit of success and fulfillment. Through eloquent writing and easily actionable steps, this book has the power to profoundly impact readers' lives.

"Having known Dr. Condon as a close friend and colleague for over 25 years, I can attest to his unparalleled commitment to advancing health and making the world a better place. As a pioneering healer, he has devoted his career to bringing true wellness to the masses. His tireless passion and determination mark him as a genuine healthcare leader, always guiding from the front with integrity. While countless books line shelves, Dr. Condon's unique blend of wisdom and action rises above, delivering a practical blueprint for realizing one's full potential. This book represents his life's work synthesizing complex ideas into illuminating and transformative insights."

Dr. Rafic Alaouie

"As a 62 year old and suffering from being hit by an 18 wheeler, I have been able to become pain free for the first time in several years. Dr. Condon literally got me out of wheelchair usage to the point of being 100% pain free. He has helped me to regain my health. Needless to say, I highly recommend Dr. Condon."

David McCarroll, CEO

INTRODUCTION

I am writing this book to serve two functions. First, my hope is to share some insights about the pursuit of success in life. And second, I hope to share my own story about that pursuit in a way that's different than a typical "success" or "self-help" book. In the end, I hope you, the reader, can be left with a different idea of what success is and know that no matter what your plan is or what business you're in, you can benefit from some of the ideas I'll be sharing. In fact, my deepest hope is that you feel compelled to pursue your own dreams for your life. I hope you become a better architect in designing the plans that give you a level of success you'll be able to enjoy and be proud of *over the course of your whole life.* This book that asks the question, "Why?" It is not so much a book about "How" to get there. One thing I've learned for sure, if you don't have a big enough reason, "a why," you should do something... you won't do it. So, now we can begin by asking some questions that might lead us all in a better direction so we can reach our goals—without compromise or contradiction.

This is where the question must be clarified. What does success really mean to us? Is it a certain amount of money? Is it producing enough to be on the Fortune 500 list? Is it living in a big house? Is it driving the fancy car? Is it sending the kids to private schools? How about the dream-vacations? In business, it's easy to look toward accounting and other metrics to understand where we are. In life, in relationships and in other pursuits it's not always clear if we are heading in the right direction until it's too late.

What this book will reveal may surprise you. There is another way. Another truth. You can have the success of your dreams and have it for the rest of your life. But if you don't keep reading you may miss out on the most important lesson in life that is required for success and long-term-fulfillment. Ultimately, the decisions we make are made in moments and those moments are cumulative. Whatever you do, wherever you live, whatever your idea of success is, I'll bet there's an element you're overlooking. You may be able to pull off a certain degree of success—even great levels of success in your business and life for a long time.

But at some point, when you're least expecting it, the Blind Spot will come for you. If you pay attention to it and abide by its demands, you will move to a level of success and happiness that you never thought possible. In fact, you may never have thought of it at all.

As you read on, please keep in mind my hope for you is that you remain calm and open to messages that are from my own experiences and from observations of some of the most "successful" people in the world. I see a common thread. I see a pattern of achievement—sometimes at levels beyond most of our ambitions. But regardless of the level of achievement, I have also at times, seen an eventual unwinding, an inevitable course of destruction, and sometimes even death. As you read on, you will see that the risks involved in not paying the Blind Spot its due, could cost you everything.

"Where there is no vision, the people perish."
—Proverbs, 29:18

THE RICHEST MAN IN THE HOSPITAL

CHAPTER 1

THINKING BACK TO MOVE AHEAD

I'm lying in bed in the hospital pissed off that I have to ask for more morphine. The nurse doesn't seem phased. She mentions something about killing elephants...all I know is that if someone doesn't take the ax out of my head, I'll need more morphine pretty quick. The nurse seems distracted and her hair is particularly frayed... reminding me of a class I took back in school that mentioned something about hair-analysis and mental illness. I'm starting to freak out about how she can't seem to draw my blood or hook up the IV. Mostly I'm just in shock that I managed to end up in the hospital... something that only happened to other people. And now I know what my neighbor was trying to warn me of...

It was a crisp, autumn day in New England. I was raking leaves in the yard, knowing I should probably be taking it easy. I had to be ready mentally and physically to see about a hundred patients the next day. I was a perfection-ist keeping up with the house and the yard. Everything had to look perfect. This was the second home we completely rehabbed to make it our own and we had just opened our second clinic. We were busy making up for all the lost time of being apart while I was in school, sacrificing everything to finally build a life and family together. The smell of the freshly cut lawn and leaves rustling by as I tried to keep up with them kept me entranced. The sun was beginning to set and the air became colder reminding me it was time to wrap things up. As I neared the end of my work, I noticed a dull headache coming on. I never got headaches and found it unusual, but mostly just annoying. I told myself I didn't have time for it. I kept working, finished up, and headed into the house where my wife was preparing a great meal. I could smell it from the porch, her classic Sicilian sauce and meatballs cooking on the stove, as it had been all day, simmering and filling the house with an incredible aroma that was only surpassed by its deep, rustic flavors. As much as I tried to ignore the headache it kept getting worse to the point where I couldn't eat. The pain persisted, and by the next day I could barely speak. The sound of my own voice was too loud to tolerate.

My wife brought me to the hospital emergency room. I remember walking in and seeing the blur of a waiting room that was completely full. Despite the number of people, I was rushed to the front of the line. I knew that taking me first, ahead of all these people, wasn't a good sign. I had been able to mumble out some words about the pain I had in my head. The next thing I knew, I was being prepped for a long needle… the nurse proceeded to do a spinal tap and said I should remain hopeful that I didn't have bacterial meningitis, "because that will probably kill you." I wasn't comforted. I was admitted and diagnosed with severe viral meningitis. I felt reassured that I wasn't dying, but the inflammation around my brain was a real problem and I stayed in the hospital for four days. I was stunned that this could happen to me. I was supposed to be a leader in health and wellness, and here I was lying in a hospital bed, down, and almost out, on a morphine drip.

It made me recall what my neighbor tried to teach me a year earlier…

"Do you want to be the richest man in the hospital?" He asked me with a concerned look that I recall was not that casual. He had watched me grow my new practice and re-hab my first home from the studs out, in just the first two years after I graduated from school. I was driven to create one the best health and wellness practices in the world, and I worked seven days a week to build it. That particular day, a Sunday, I had some time later in the afternoon and had decided to start cleaning up the leaves in the yard. It was a cold day in November and the leaves were wet and heavy as I feverishly raked and bagged them up. I was also intent on not having anything out of order; the yard had to look good. I was obsessed with success and controlling my environment at all times. My neighbor, who was a retired man in his seventies, kindly tried to bring my attention to something he thought I was missing. He knew that I wasn't seeing the fact that I had a blind-spot, I was so focused on achievement in some areas of my life, that I was setting myself up for a rude awakening if I didn't slow down. Little did I know how prophetic he would be.

Once I came to terms with the fact that I would have to become better, more self-aware, and that I would have to learn to accept being uncomfortable and humbled, everything got a lot easier. I was completely focused on the end-result and nothing less would be acceptable. I had always read books about success in life and business. And as you might guess, one of my favorites was *The Richest Man in Babylon*, by George Clason. After receiving the lesson from my neighbor, I went back to reading that book again to see how I would feel about business and financial success at that point, after all the lessons and successes I had so early in my career. But now I had the layer of being hospitalized, blindsided by an infection that I thought could never happen to me. I knew I had to figure out my priorities and find a way to embrace success in life and business without compromising my health.

As I read through *The Richest Man in Babylon* again, I began to realize some new things and see other things I had missed the first time. There was a conspicuous lack of discussion on the topic of health being a part of one's asset portfolio. This wake-up call made me realize that I could choose a different path. I realized that I had neglected the basic tenets I had always taught—that life and health and true happiness and success happened "on-purpose" and not "by accident." I was reminded that my health had to be a major focus in my personal growth and development. Being healthy was a possibility for everyone. I knew I was born to be healthy, and I had always preached in my practices that we each have incredible health potential and that a life without fear, sickness, and disease was possible. I had always taught that focusing on health and removing interference was the key, not waiting for symptoms to treat, living in fear of disease, while ignoring causes. I knew my biggest obstacle was myself and I knew that I had to get to work on building a system and plan for my wellness that was congruent with all my values—including being a successful doctor and helping others and myself at the same time. I knew I WAS THE CAUSE of my disease and inability to be well in all ways. What I realized so clearly was that I needed to remove the contradictions between my thoughts and actions to create new and better outcomes. It was a simple epiphany, but I tend to think most things in life are simple in their truest form. We tend to complicate things, and when we do, we lose sight of the original vision or purpose.

One thing I noticed about myself was that I was only working at the superficial parts of being healthy. I was staying reasonably fit and had a home-gym built so I was consistently working out a few days a week. But I had been indulging too much in bad habits—too much junk food, sweets, and going out to eat too often. I had gained about twenty pounds and was the guy who thought he looked better than he did. And that was really the problem. I was basing my health on how I looked and felt. The crazy thing is, I didn't look or feel that great anyway. I was losing no matter how I tried to fool myself. I took an inventory of my behavior and saw a pattern of neglect and denial. I basically had to admit I was living in contradiction to my own stated values. I knew that health was God-given but that I had to be the steward of my health and that meant my **lifestyle and values had to be congruent.**

As a student while in chiropractic school, I studied philosophy as well as many science courses of anatomy, physiology, radiology, etc. One particular doctor had outlined the importance of living in alignment with our stated philosophy and that when we failed to do this, or lived in contradiction to it, we would experience a level of destruction equal to the level of the contradiction we were living in. He had cited Ayn Rand as his basis to this conclusion, and it made a lot of sense to me back then and even more now. It was obvious that the laws of the Universe did not cease to exist in my body. I recalled the basic five branches of philosophy which in a practical sense are these:

1. **Metaphysics:** Essentially asking the question of ourselves, "Where am I?" In the context of our health it would be asking, "Where is my current level of health?" This demonstrates the nature of our view of reality.

2. **Epistemology:** This asks the question, "How do I know?"

3. **Ethics:** This asks the question, "What do I do?"

4. **Politics:** This branch demonstrates the action or force used to carry out the ethical basis.

5. **Aesthetics:** This is how we dress things up or how we make things look on the outside.

What I learned by assessing this philosophical premise was that we all carry a philosophy around with us. We use it as a guide every day in our thoughts and actions. Ultimately, our philosophy dictates not only our thoughts and actions, but our outcomes. Many people have never studied this and are unaware that they have a basic philosophical premise for their actions. At worst, this can prove to be a fatal flaw in our lives as it can lead us to destinations we don't desire . At best, we may tend to take two steps forward and three steps backward in attempting to reach our goals without realizing that our philosophy or "blueprint" for living, may be clouded with contradictions that hold us back.

I was living this way. I was clear in my mind that health came from above-down, inside-out. This meant that all that I needed to be and stay healthy was given to me by God and ran through my nervous system to all body parts and systems. I knew I didn't need any help. I just needed no interference, and I could be well over the span of my lifetime. The problem was, **I was creating the interference.** I was not eating properly, not resting enough, not getting enough exercise, not paying attention to my own posture and spinal health, and not drinking enough water. You might think these things are trivial and I'm overstating the need for a shift in behavior... but I did end up in the hospital, and there's always a cause!

Basically, I was violating all the basics I was teaching my patients to pay attention to. And this is a great lesson. No matter how educated we are, it will not help us if we don't take the right action. This is why the expression, "knowledge is power" is not completely true. Knowledge is only powerful if we use it. Knowledge is *potential power*. When we want to become more powerful, we must implement strategies and actions to reach our intended goals. *Implementation is power.* Taking action is power. And when we align our philosophy with CONGRUENT ACTION, we get the desired result or outcome we are looking to achieve.

The other element of knowledge that can deter us from achieving our goals is that we can have the wrong knowledge. My situation was not that I had the wrong knowledge. I just failed to implement. But what if my knowledge was wrong and my philosophical premise dictated a metaphysical view of reality that I was well as long as I looked and felt good? I did think I was well just before I got sick with meningitis. My epistemological response to "how do I know?" (if I was healthy) was answered internally by my thoughts of how I felt and how I thought I looked. Not to mention no one else was saying, "Hey are you feeling okay?" or, "Hey it looks like you've put on a few pounds!" So, I thought I was just great. My ethical response to my daily habits about, "What do I do?" was simple... nothing. I just kept on going and pushing to reach my goals. So, the idea is we can deter ourselves if we have the wrong premise. I realized this is where I was living and where most of my patients were living... in a place of denial.

I knew there was a better solution, and I was forced into a reality check that brought me back to basics and God's plans for me. I knew that by abiding in God's laws and staying close to Him and all He provided, I had all the tools necessary to live vitally well into my 100s. I had known this innately since childhood. As an adult, and having studied all the basic sciences, and then receiving my doctorate degree in chiropractic school, I was ready to share that idea with the whole world. One of the most important lessons I learned in school was that the right philosophy was critical in forming the framework or blueprints necessary for success. I also knew that any contradictions in my philosophical premises would undermine my success. The guiding laws were a basic outline:

The Laws of Life and Health that are God-given and indisputable are the following:

1. The human body is a self-healing, self-regulating organism.

2. The central nerve system is the master-system and controller of the body.

3. Any interference with that system will cause a decrease in the body's ability to heal and regulate.

Suddenly, I realized I was in love with these principles or laws. I could see clearly how simple it was and that health and maintenance of health wasn't a mystery. It became obvious that I had taken this for granted. It was as if it was too simple to even take seriously and that I had begun to ignore them. It reminded me of an Aldous Huxley quote, "A truth does not cease to exist because it is ignored." To think… I was BORN with more intelligence in one second than my EDUCATED intelligence would ever realize in my lifetime!

God says, "My people are destroyed from lack of knowledge."
—Hosea 4:6

What also became clear was that the simple truth was just one factor to be considered in my metaphysical view of what it meant to be well. Abiding by these truths was the hard part because it required behavior changes. And for anyone who has disciplined themselves to make major changes in their health over a long period of time, you know it isn't easy. To hold myself accountable for where

I went wrong was one thing, but doing what it took to turn my life and health around would be different levels of challenges to overcome. I knew where the contradictions were, but I also knew that now I was going to be in a fight against myself. I knew I would have to face the demons that threatened my success, my life, my health, and my family's well-being.

Recognizing the interference in all its forms was a critical step. The demons of weak priorities, distraction, and contradiction. Forgetting my responsibility to God for caring for the incredible gifts of life and health He gave me was my biggest mistake, and sadly, one I see most people make. I had identified the demons that led me away from abiding in the laws of life and health. I broke them down into a few basic flaws that were among the seven deadly sins:

1. Fear

2. Pride

3. Gluttony

I could see how fear led me away from God's plans for me. I could see how fear was the opposite of faith. And I could see that fear was just self-doubt. My identity was keeping me stuck in a place of fear. Who was I to be this great leader in my community? Would I be able to really lead the masses of people and bring them to the answers they were looking for? And besides, there were so many others more qualified than I. And there were so many other leaders already that were already famous for their work. Why would anyone listen to me? Sure, I was able to build a couple of busy clinics seeing hundreds of patients visits each week, but shifting the course of healthcare in my community or even around the country were ridiculous goals—so I told myself.

I could also see how my pride got in the way. I was too proud to face those fears and to share them and to seek the necessary help to get beyond them. I figured if I was the authority in my field I was projecting to be, I should already have had the answers. And in a way, I think gluttony played a role in the interference. I would settle into the idea that I was already successful. I already achieved more than most, I would tell myself. I had the successful practices, the beautiful wife and kids, the nice home, and cars, and vacations... all the stuff I thought equaled success. I quickly learned how wrong I was to neglect my greatest asset—my health. The irony was that it was all an illusion and one I had been forced to reckon with. I began to see that my definition of success was misplaced and that I had a blind-spot that finally caught up with me and caught me off guard. I knew I didn't have much time to fix this thing—there was no way I was going to be in the hospital for long I told myself—much less "take it easy for the next six months or so," as the nurses and doctors cautioned me to do.

When was there a time in your life when took pause to reflect, knowing you were in a moment of self-discovery that could bring you to the "next-level"?

When you recognized that moment, did you "catalogue" it in writing or into your consciousness?

> ACTION STEP: When confronted with a new sense of reality, keep a journal entry of it and note how it made you feel. Notice how you came up with your own conclusion and then decide and write down what to do about it. By doing this, you start to realize your own innate power to improve your life.

THE RICHEST MAN IN THE HOSPITAL

CHAPTER 2

NOBODY IS COMING TO RESCUE YOU

I t was a new opportunity to dial into my own health and I knew I had to accomplish this with some re-search first. I knew I would have to quickly learn what was necessary in order to not only avoid the blind-spot of sickness and disease, but I would have to discover how to maximize my health, and how to achieve a new level that would keep me well over my lifetime. I went head-first into the discovery process. I knew that health was more than the absence of sickness or symptoms. I had watched so many patients over the years who looked well, suddenly get diagnosed with cancer and be gone within a year or so. My own uncle, who had a history of great health, looked great and was super-fit, died after he was diagnosed with stage-four pancreatic cancer. It was startling and devastating. He had never had a major ill-ness. until one day he woke up and was terminally ill. .
Six months later, he was dead. He was only 60 years old. The best doctors in Boston couldn't do anything for him. I

soon watched his daughter, my cousin, die from leukemia. She was just 35 years old, and left behind her husband and two small children. And soon after that, a close friend would succumb to cancer. And over, and over again over the years I've taken care of so many patients who were widows (mostly women) who had lost their husbands to some variety of disease. To say my health-awareness was elevated would be an understatement. I knew I was being tested to learn something. And was acutely aware that if I continued down the path I was on, I would likely get sick again. And the next time, it could be more serious—even deadly. I also knew not to blame God or my genetics. I knew that God gave me all I needed to heal, function, and operate at 100%, As long as I trusted that and became a better caretaker of what He gave me, I could reach my potential. *After all,* I thought to myself, *we humans are the only animals on Earth that exhibit chronic disease. No other animal in nature, left to its normal habits and environment reveals such sickness—just us humans.* The more I thought about this, the more absurd and tragic it all seemed. *Why would God make us in His image, only to be weaker than a humming bird?*

I set out to define the key steps necessary to build a healthy immune system. I would read many books on subjects ranging from diet, nutrition, exercise, naturopathy, chiropractic care, supplementation, and other articles related to overall wellness. I became particularly interested in the science and area of biology that focused on our epigenetics. The focus was essentially that our DNA doesn't dictate our health by itself but that our lifestyle or environment we put our cells in, will interface with our cell membranes and either allow for certain DNA switches to be turned on or off expressing our traits. I had already learned so much in school and in practice, and with some newer research, but I had to dig deeper to be sure I was armed with the latest and best data to use. The biggest take-away was learning that it wouldn't be good enough to just try to avoid being sick. I knew the blind-spot was way bigger than that. I would find myself thinking that if someone wanted to get sick, they could guarantee it by living like the average American. As I looked at the diet and looked at what was considered permissible by the FDA to exist on store shelves for human consumption, I realized a completely different lifestyle would be necessary.

I knew the organic food industry was on the rise for a good reason. And I started to make connections between the drug ads we see on TV and the foods people eat every day. I realized too that in most other countries, GMO foods were illegal and drug ads were not allowed on TV. It was compelling to read articles about how GMO foods were linked to tumor growth and infertility. These are very common problems in our country as so many people are now getting cancer and so many are resorting to fertility treatments to start a family. I also began to make connections with so many common illnesses and the nutrient-deprived diets most of my patients and I had. And

I thought, *isn't it interesting that there is one governing body called the FDA—the Food and Drug Administration, that oversees both?* It suddenly became obvious to me—the fox has been guarding the henhouse!

The blind-spot was beginning to get smaller and smaller as I was seeing a light of truth about what health really was all about. I was seeing that our whole health-care model was severely broken. I was seeing contradictions in the policies and realities that govern our health and create the outcomes of so much sickness. I was seeing that it was impossible to achieve my highest health-potential following the "rules" that we have all been taught. I was certain the game of life and health was rigged. And it started with the faulty premise that health was an outside-in phenomenon. That somehow, if we just followed FDA and CDC guidelines and our doctor's orders, we could be well. But what I learned was that we as a nation, are spending more on "healthcare" than all other industrialized nations combined, but rank at or near the bottom in almost every significant category from infant mortality to life-expectancy. I also learned that the number one cause of preventable death in the U.S. was iatrogenic disease, meaning, doctor-caused! It was suddenly obvious that our healthcare system and its governing agencies are essentially captured in place by the pharmaceutical industry to keep the citizens sick and dependent on them to treat the diseases we are creating. Not only are these agencies aligned philosophically, but politically as well. And their conflicts of interest prevent them from promoting health and wellness, much less saving anybody.

I was peeling back the layers of contradiction in the system and seeing first-hand how by following it, friends and family were dying and how by going in a completely opposite direction, my family was beginning to thrive. It was the beginning of a true awakening. I knew I had to lead my family and patients away from the level of thinking they had toward a new model or philosophical premise or paradigm that was biased toward self-responsibility and reliance on our own innate intelligence. The new model would eliminate the blind-spot and enable us all to live the life of health, healing, and abundance we were born to live. Removing contradictions in our lives would be the key to unlocking the mystery of true success so many of us strive for. It was time to save ourselves—knowing no one else could.

At what points in your life have you recognized your own mistakes and at the same time realized you were at fault?

Can you see times when you had blind spots that caught you off guard that you could have prevented?

Are you willing to take responsibility for your actions and outcomes?

> ACTION STEP: When you can see your blind spots recognize how they got there and make choices to

position yourself better the next time. Anticipate challenges, confrontations and denials and be prepared to handle them. Most of all, ready yourself to live in a place of self-control that will enable you to better see what contradiction looks like in others and yourself when you fall short.

CHAPTER 3

THE POTENTIAL POWER OF KNOWLEDGE

S oon after this period of awakening, I realized that even though I had new knowledge, I was seeing that it was very challenging to even share it with others, much less, get them to do anything with it. My family was different because they had already lived through the experience of implementing massive lifestyle changes that ultimately helped all of us overcome limitations or blind-spots and maintain our health. The interesting and challenging part was getting my patients to change their behavior. I was amazed that educated and intelligent people were practically unable to hear a different message of health, hope, and healing than what they had previously learned growing up.

What I began to understand was this phenomenon of being unable to learn new things when the new things were the opposite of what they thought was true. The term for this phenomenon is called, cognitive dissonance, and it can trap you in a stifled, limited state of education and existence. Cognitive Dissonance is defined this way; In the field of psychology, cognitive dissonance occurs when a person is presented with two or more contradictory beliefs, ideas, or values, or participates in an action that goes against one of these three, and experiences psychological stress because of that. An example of this is when Christopher Columbus said the world wasn't flat. He knew he would voyage out to sea and prove that the world wasn't flat. People wanted to kill him just for having a different idea! The same thing happened with the man who first stated it was important to do regular handwashing to prevent the spread of different kinds of infectious diseases. His name was Dr. Ignaz Semmelweis, an Austrian physician who was ostracized for his ideas on hand-hygiene. It's reported he was so ridiculed by the medical establishment, that he suffered a breakdown and was put into an asylum and beaten severely by the guards there. He died shortly thereafter. Years following his death, Luis Pasteur, corroborated the hygienic practices Dr. Semmelweis had advocated and now these practices are considered the standard of care and critical in the world of medicine and surgery. The stress people have ultimately caused them an inability to accept new information and therefore, limits change, growth, and often, success.

Today, we face the same challenges in the world of healthcare. It was not that long ago that the profession of chiropractic was maligned by the AMA for "practicing medicine without a license." At that time, many chiropractors went to prison for standing up to the AMA to practice their unique, distinct profession of spinal care. Years later, and as recently as 1987, the chiropractic profession was forced to file an anti-trust lawsuit against the AMA. The chiropractic profession was victorious at the Supreme Court level and a permanent injunction was levied against the AMA to cease and desist in their efforts to conspire to contain and eliminate the chiropractic profession. Yet, even during an explosion of new research and scientific advancements within the chiropractic profession, coupled with their legal victories in court, there remains a social stigma that prevents many patients from seeking advice from chiropractors. The profession has gained some acceptance worldwide and patients of chiropractic care report a 95% satisfaction rate overall. Research has proven impressive results with chiropractic care in cases involving ear infections, infertility, and headaches to name just a few. But most people are reluctant to deviate from what they know—even if the data supporting what they know reveals a less desirable track-record.

When it comes to choosing our healthcare, we must ask a few pertinent questions. The paradigm or model of healthcare that we choose is based upon certain premises. These ideas have been taught to us over the course of our lifetime. Usually, we get these ideas from our parents and our doctors. But what if the lessons they are teaching us are wrong? Could it be that the people we admire, respect, and love the most are misleading us? What if the information and knowledge they've been given is all wrong? These questions remind me again of Rand's idea... she famously stated that, "Wherever there are contradictions, there will be destruction, and the level of destruction will always equal the level of contradiction."

The notion that many of us hold contradictions in our health-philosophy is what leads me to examine, more closely, what health is. Because if we have contradictions in our health-philosophy, and the outcome is destruction... we must surmise that we may be making choices to be healthy, but those choices are making us more and more sick! We can have all the information from the "best" doctors and the "best" research, but if the philosophical basis of that knowledge proposes to keep us healthy is founded upon reactive, symptom-based treatment protocols, are we getting closer to health?

Is the pursuit of better treatment options for sickness and disease the same as gaining knowledge to stay healthy?

What we now have, in our advanced society as Americans, is a system of sickness and dis-ease care that is unparalleled anywhere in the world. The very system we rely upon for better health, from the supposed best doctors and hospitals in the world, is really a system of sick-care or disease-care, not healthcare. The AMA has successfully cornered the market (you and me) on the business of controlling what the standard of care should be in our healthcare model. Keep in mind, the AMA is a lobbying group comprised mainly of pharmaceutical representatives, not doctors. The AMA owns the diagnosis and treatment codes used by all physicians including Doctors of Chiropractic. This might explain why a medical physician is paid more for the same procedure than a chiropractic physician. It's also interesting to note that there is a term used by insurance companies and the AMA that is the criteria for determining what evaluations and treatments are covered by insurance. The language used is "medically necessary." This means typically, that most chiropractic, homeopathic, acupuncture or other forms of care are not covered as they are deemed by the powers that be, not medically necessary. Only a small percentage of coverage is available to those disciplines—just enough to provide an umbilical cord of dependency and ultimately, enough to keep those professions from growing as competition to the pharmaceutical industry.

So, now we see we have a model of care we rely upon to stay healthy, but the model is reactive, not proactive. It's a model of treatment of sickness and disease with drugs and surgery. The last time I checked, drugs aren't good for you. They've never been purported to create health. After all, we don't lose our health due to a deficiency of drugs in our blood or having too many organs! The information and knowledge we've been given has led us further and further away from health each year over the last century and a half. When we compare our health-status to all other industrialized nations, we show up incredibly low on the ranking's lists. If the information we've been given was right, that it would lead us to better health, we wouldn't be coming in near last place in almost every category. Imagine if the premise of the current model were based upon logic and was true healthcare, the person taking the most prescription drugs would be considered the healthiest! Unfortunately, this is the exact model we've been taught to accept. In fact, if you've noticed, there are more drug ads on TV these days than any other form of advertising. This behavior is systematically brainwashing generations to accept that better health is derived through better chemistry. Simultaneously though, we see increasing numbers of morbidity and mortality from obesity, diabetes, heart-disease, and cancer. So, how did that Ayn Rand quote go...? Perhaps this is why it is illegal in most other developed nations outside of the U.S. to allow for drug-ads directly to the consumer. Can you think of another product advertised to you that is for your benefit, that you cannot purchase on your own, without the authority of someone else determining whether you should have it or not?

I think it's obvious that we are in a real crisis. Would you agree? We have massive contradictions in our philosophy that governs our healthcare decisions and these contradictions have led to massive destruction. While we have made great advances in delivering more drugs to more people than ever, we have a society that is sicker than ever.

It's an utterly unsustainable model and we can see its burden on the insurance industry, hospitals, and most importantly, on the patients. What we must do is ask different questions like, "What is health?" Where does health come from?" "How do I preserve my state of health or improve it?" These answers won't come from the "best doctors." The best doctors you know are the ones you have been taught to seek advice from, and they are not the health experts. They are the disease experts. To get the answers you need, you must go to those with the most training and expertise in those fields.

For example, the chiropractic physician has been trained with the following premise:

- That health is relative to the vitalistic expression of the whole person.
- That the human being is greater than the sum of its parts.
- That unlike a mechanistic point of view, the expression of life and the experience of being alive goes beyond our body parts and systems—there is a vitalistic element that is less obvious.

The major premise being that the body is a self-healing, self-regulating organism and the brain and spinal-cord, known as the central nerve-system, is the master system and controller of the body. Therefore, through deductive logic, one must surmise that any interference with that system would cause the body to have a diminished ability to self-heal and self-regulate. This is a compelling notion for understanding where health comes from. And we can easily see how if we could manage to take care of the nerve-system, we would likely be able to function at a higher level.

Part of taking care of that system is recognizing how it is interfered with. There are physical, mental, emotional, chemical, and even spiritual ways we can interfere with the nerve system. We also know there are certain nutritional requirements to remain well. A human can only go a few weeks or so without any food. Only a few days without any water. Only a matter a minutes without oxygen. And just think, when a nerve is damaged completely, the organ or muscle supplied by that nerve dies instantly. Perhaps this is why the medical neurologist is so keen on testing nerve-function. Don't they know this information? So, why don't they recommend chiropractic care to their patients more often? After all, chiropractic physicians are uniquely trained on how to detect and correct the spinal misalignments that have been proven to reduce nerve-function. And when we look at the education of a chiropractic physician versus a medical physician, the curricula are almost identical except that chiropractors study *more* hours in anatomy, physiology, diagnosis, radiology, and neurology. They then go on to learn the science and art of manual spinal manipulation or "adjustment" through clinical interaction with patients while the medical physician goes through a residency program to learn patient care in a hospital setting. Both types of physicians must be board-certified before being licensed to practice.

As you look at the landscape of our healthcare system and the emphasis placed on drugs and surgery, you can see you have a certain degree of information and understanding that is incomplete if you're looking for what it takes to be healthy. I have spent decades sharing with my patients all I know about wellness, nutrition, exercise, and the relationships between the structure and function of the body. I have seen cases where patients have come into my office as a last resort, looking for the keys to unlocking their health-potential. They all have different stories. They all have different family histories. But what they all have had in common is a level of frustration and knowing that there must be answers they just haven't been able to find. They all intuitively know that the body is supposed to heal itself. They just don't know how to bridge the gap between what they've always known and what they know must exist. As we move forward in this book we will see how a simple shift in consciousness can lead us down a different path—one that illuminates truth in its simplest form—that the right knowledge, **applied** the right way at the right time, will be the power to bringing us closer to success in all areas of our lives.

Can you recognize any time(s) in your life when you thought you knew something and then found out new information that changed your mind?

Have you ever been confronted on your set of values or ideas about a subject and found yourself uncomfortable defending your ideas?

> ACTION STEP: When you are convinced that you know everything there is to know about your position or ideas, ask yourself, "Is it possible I could have missed out on some information or research because I really just *want* to believe in what I believe?
>
> Put your ego aside and take joy and peace in knowing no one knows everything. You have the right to be a work in progress! Find out as much as you can about all sides of a story and then make up your own mind after you've done your own research and been able to sift through others' opinions.

CHAPTER 4

TAKING THE RISK OF BEING HEALTHY

Now that you're hopefully asking better questions and getting better answers, you have a chance. You can literally start over right now with your own decisions about how to stay on the right track in life. Your prioritization of your health should be advancing on your success-hierarchy. Your shift in consciousness may have already happened now that you've read the previous chapters. The only question now is, "What are you going to do about it?" You might ask, "What is the right-track?" The right track is the one that keeps you moving forward toward achieving your potential. You were born with a certain potential that is likely only limited by your own imagination and by the thinking you've already been programmed with. To continue growing into your full potential, you must have your mind made up that you will be open to new information and then be willing to put in the work necessary to use it. There are risks involved, however. If you continue your current path, will you make progress? And if you do, will it be great progress or incremental progress or no progress at all?

The only way to grow is to know and then, *act*. The risks involved are massive. If you stay the same, statistics show you will achieve mediocre success in business, in your relationships, and certainly, with your health, if you're lucky. The inextricable truth is that your success is tied to your philosophy. If you have contradictions in your philosophy and in how you live, you will see commensurate levels of failure. This chapter is inserted for you to take a moment to reflect on your current strategy for achieving the success you want in life. When it comes to your health, ask yourself, "Is following what I've always done working for me? Is taking a symptom-based approach to treating sickness and disease bringing me closer to my health-potential?" You can't expect different results by doing the same things. If you recognize now that you may have built ideas on faulty premises and you can see that you've struggled to achieve things in life that are important to you, then you've succeeded in step one. And if you understand how this impacts your "health-success," you're really advancing along in this discovery journey!

Whether it's our business, our relationships, or our own health, it's easy to see how effects become the focus rather than the causes leaving no opportunity for correction or growth.

Here's where the risk comes in. If we remain the same, no one will notice. The most dangerous place to be is "normal," or average. If you live in the normal space, you'll be sure to fit right in with everyone. Ever since you were a kid you tried to fit in, didn't you? Maybe your parents thought it was good for you to fit in too, so they made sure to buy you all the "right" clothes, the ones your friends were wearing. You went to the "right" schools. You were likely taught not to talk about money or politics or religion with anyone. Eventually you just learned to keep everything inside and not ever talk about the very things most important to all of us. In the context of your health, if you consistently lose fitness over the years and begin building the need for taking more and more medications to treat symptoms, sickness, and disease, unfortunately, you will fit right into our society in general. Sadly, our culture has taken an attitude of accepting sickness being more normal than health! To be different requires you to risk letting go of ideas and practices that have not brought you closer to reaching your health potential.

Nowadays, it appears the road to becoming your own true-self, striving to reach your own potential, creates the thing we've always tried to avoid—the haters. Most of us have spent our lives desperately trying to fit in and be accepted by our peers. "Keeping up with the Joneses," is a phrase that comes to mind. But have we sold-out on our own potential? The people I've come across in my own life that have achieved the most in their work, their health, and their relationships are the people who don't care about fitting in. They are the ones who have taken the biggest risks—mainly to just do what they want and to do what they feel is right for them.

That kind of behavior reminds me of another idea of Rand's... the "virtue of selfishness." But why not be selfish when it comes to living our lives the way we want? If we are not hurting anyone else and making positive contributions to society, how can we be faulted? Why should "fitting in" be the standard that's acceptable? Ever notice that when you want to change for the better it often makes those around you uncomfortable? They'll say things to you like, "Hey don't work too hard...", or when you've decided to try a cleaner diet, "Hey, since when did you become a health-nut?" Or how about when you decide to dial into your responsibilities—you are now a "control-freak!"

The risk occurs when you decide to forego the rest of the pack...

When you decide not to follow the herd and break out into creating the best YOU, you can be!

"Make the most of yourself,
for that is all there is of you."
—Ralph Waldo Emerson

Being true to yourself, armed with the right information, unfettered by contradictions, will allow you to transform your life.

When you've made commitments to yourself to make the changes necessary for your growth, and you've abandoned being average and "fitting-in," you will spend the necessary energy and resources to get the life you want by taking the risks of thinking outside the box and independently of an effect-focus and more to a cause-focus mentality when managing your daily healthcare needs.

When it comes to your personal healthcare and daily wellness practices, you must remain aware of being proactive and not get lulled into complacency assuming you're healthy just because you feel good. Pain is the last thing to show up in the dis-ease cycle. Lab findings will often remain negative until there's significant disease in the body.

Over the years, I've seen thousands of patients and heard the story more times than I can recount, how they bent forward to pick up a sock off the floor and felt a "pop" in their back or neck. They then were in debilitating pain as they came into my office. After ruling out any prior history of injuries or similar events, I would ask them, "Do you really think that bending down to pick a sock up off the floor should do this to you?" Of course, they understood that it shouldn't have happened. But getting caught off guard by the Blind-Spot is easy if you have missed some details of how to stay well. It invariably requires the risk of adopting a different health-philosophy!

Ask yourself, "Am I in control of myself?" "Am I in control of my healthcare decisions?"

You will discover you're either in control or you're not.

Self-directed, In-Control behavior is when you've made choices that reflect your values and the information you have researched on your own. Don't take other's opinions as matters of fact—no matter their pedigree. Look at the actual data and research (peer-reviewed, RCT) and be okay with it even if it points you in an unexpected direction.

> ACTION STEP: Gather your information into your own personal library and arsenal of intellectual ammunition so you can rationally (not emotionally) defend your point of view.
>
> Next, use this as your platform to go about your life, personal healthcare and even a way to share information with friends and family who may be stuck in a certain pattern or way of thinking based upon others' opinions and ideas.

CHAPTER 5

THE PICASSO PRINCIPLE

With my new-found clarity and sense of purpose reawakened, I had discovered that contradictions led to my failures and those small mis-steps over time were what caught me off-guard. I also got reacquainted with the basic philosophy of life and health that I knew would be the right knowledge to move forward without fear. I recalled a lesson from one of my favorite teachers, Dr. Fred Barge, who said, **"Fear is the Fuel that Fires the Furnace of Disease."** I could see how fear was so destructive and to remove dis-ease and restore ease would accelerate my ability to reach my goals.

This also reminded me of an important lesson. It was called the Picasso Principle. The Principle was based upon a story that went something like this: Once upon a time, there was a man walking along the street in a quaint village somewhere in Italy when he came upon an artist painting what looked to be an abstract of some kind of natural landscape. When the man realized the artist was none other than Pablo Picasso, he excitedly exclaimed, "What a beautiful work this is sir... I must have it! I will pay whatever you ask, just name your price." When Picasso turned and named his price the man was shocked. He asked, "How can you ask for such a sum? I watched you paint this almost from beginning to end... it only took you approximately an hour." Picasso turned to him and replied, "That is where you are wrong my friend. You see, it has taken me a lifetime."

The lesson was that what may have appeared to be so simple was really a level of expertise demonstrated efficiently and gracefully by a great artist. What we see on the surface and perceive immediately is the apparent result of recent effort. The reality is that almost everything in life that causes proficiency and great success is the result of many lessons and great diligence.

In designing this new life, I knew I would have to take these tough lessons I learned and apply them without regard for immediate gratification. I knew the Blind-Spot came for me due to a lack of implementation that created an imbalance in my life. I knew I would have to recall the story of Picasso in my mind and that the graceful rendition of my new life would come from many hours of work and repetition and that my ultimate success in reaching all my goals would begin and end with my actions every day for the next several decades. This too brought up another life lesson I had heard along the way and filed into my memory somewhere along the journey... *Perseverance alone, is omnipotent.*

I realized then how important this idea was. The reality was that all the lessons were already there and wisdom to know what was true. The problem was that I had ignored the truth, and like so many people, would allow for challenges to remain unsolved and let contradictions creep in. I wasn't any different than the patients I cared for. I looked to remain comfortable, to avoid pain, and seek pleasure. The irony I was realizing was that the life, health, and success I wanted was all inside the space of being uncomfortable. The level of discomfort would be like a thermostat in my life, guiding my actions as it would never allow me to go beyond my identity. I knew that I would have to acknowledge and accept that my destiny would rest in my identity or how I identified MYSELF. I would have to accept that God had given me the gifts and tools I needed to BE all that I needed, to DO whatever was required, and to HAVE whatever life I wanted. It was always up to me, and it's always up to you. Just don't expect everything to happen overnight!

The Picasso Principle was a reminder of the lesson of persistence and finding joy in the process. I knew that everything that would ultimately be great in my life, including my health, would come one step at a time, and would pose real and uncomfortable challenges that would force me to reach my potential if I could just get out of my own way!

The cumulative steps required would not necessarily be taken in the shortest distance between two points but would be challenged with side-steps and even some backward steps as I navigated and created more clarity as I went. I learned to accept the journey for what it was and that no matter how uncomfortable I might be, I would press on and not allow myself to stay at a lower temperature just to remain comfortable. It was time to reset the thermostat of my life and get comfortable being uncomfortable. This, I knew, was the necessary requirement to get to the next level. I also knew to become a Picasso, I would have to become a master of my life, my health, and my destiny. I knew that God made us all to be our own versions of Picasso, to bring greatness to the world with our unique gifts, and to render ourselves as His masterpieces to share with each other.

Armed with a reborn sense of purpose and perspective, I decided the way of life moving forward had to have a well-defined strategy backed up with a clear philosophy and executed without contradiction, at least for the most part. My new perspective was that I realized I already had what I needed and that I just needed no interference. I also believed then, and still do today, that it's not necessary to be perfect to reach our goals in life. To be healthy, I knew I had to recalibrate what it meant to be healthy and what each day would look like to get and maintain health. The redesign would keep the Picasso Principle alive within me and act as a guide to allow for growth without guilt. I would learn to be at peace with the journey but on-purpose at all times. In other words, if I decided to eat a piece of pizza or have a glass of wine it would be intentional. I would be aware of the moment, enjoy it, know I was enjoying it, and that it would be okay because it was a treat. I thought about how I had gotten off course and that too many days became treat-days. I had fallen into the common thought process and behavioral acceptance of the, everything in moderation, mentality. The result was moderate health. Moderate or average health resulted in being run-down when I ramped up the thermostat. My body could not tolerate being driven like a Ferrari with regular gas in the tank!

Step one would consist of revamping the diet. I knew from years of weight-training and bodybuilding that I would have to get back to basics. I decided to cut out sugar and all forms of processed foods, snacks, etc. I made the daily intake food charts and made sure to include only lean, clean sources of animal protein as well as non-GMO, organic sources of vegetable proteins. I decided to keep my carbohydrate intake lower for a while to stimulate fat metabolism and I began taking in plenty of healthy fats in the form of nuts, avocado, and fish oil etc. I knew that tracking when I ate, what I ate, how much I ate, and how frequently I ate would be a good starting point. I also knew myself well enough to know that I needed to keep it simple. If I over-thought this part and tried to get fancy with a bunch of different new meals and recipes I would fall off the wagon pretty quickly. I decided I would eat like a bodybuilder —following a diet that was fairly bland and simple so I wouldn't have to think much about what I would need. As I recount this time of my life, I realize that this diet strategy may not be a one-size-fits-all strategy but it would likely work for the majority of people especially as a jumpstart if nothing else. As I wrote this chapter though, I also realized that I still tended to follow this strategy for the most part and have had great success maintaining a healthier body composition and weight for over two decades.

Sometimes you have to just figure out a way to keep it simple—set it and forget it. Ultimately, I think it's best to graduate to a mind-set of looking at food as fuel for performance. In order for this to occur, you have to realize you'll be constantly challenged by a cultural trend of being led by our gut for entertainment. The food and eating culture of approaching food and food preparation as entertainment is adding to a waistline problem in our society. With a new cooking show on tv seemingly every other month, and new cookbooks and blogs posted constantly, and a going out to eat culture that has made eating at home a rare event, it's easy to see how people are facing serious health and weight challenges. The food industry is not driven to increase your health. It's masterful in creating food-addictions and behavioral changes that pre-destine societies' ills.

To combat the societal trend of eating for entertainment and to learn to eat to live rather than live to eat, takes some time and patience with ourselves. Implementing a diet rich in nutrients with "food by God" instead of a diet that is high in calories but low in nutrients ("food by man") is a great place to start. Day by day, month over month, and eventually year to year, we can see the cumulative constructive benefits outweighing the cumulative destructive habits. Your artistic rendering of a new life of abundant health and accomplishment will come in time as you recall the Picasso Principle along the journey.

Ask yourself, "Where am I now and where do I want to go?" "Has anybody ever done what I want to do?" "Am I willing to do whatever it takes (remaining lawful and ethical) to get there even if it makes me uncomfortable?"

By defining these things you can set yourself on a clear path for success.

> ACTION STEP: Answer the questions above and choose a mentor who has done what you want to do. Get their help. Study what they did and what they do now. Take notes and when possible, see if you can shadow them or get coaching from them.

ACTION STEP: Once you've observed their methods and learned from what they did, write down your goals. You've seen what is possible. Now go do it and track yourself. By writing down your goals you will remain clearer and more focused and more able to achieve them.

CHAPTER 6

RE-DEFINING SUCCESS

---

*"You cannot solve a problem with the same
thinking you had when the problem was
created."*

—Albert Einstein

In the introduction to this book you will recall that I suggested you may be surprised by what you were about to read. Maybe some of what you have read conjures up some of those feelings of imbalance I had mentioned or maybe you are starting to evaluate some of your own decisions about your life and your health. If that is the case, then I am succeeding in my quest to help you re-define how you look at success and fulfillment in your own life. Even if you've been able to achieve great things in your academic pursuits, in your relationships or in business, if you've missed out on the biggest part of your success journey, you're probably less effective and happy than you could be. You may notice, it can be difficult to perform at a high level when you're fatigued or not well.

By adding the element of proactive self-care and a focus on your health to your success-radar, you will see how much further you can go!

As a health and wellness advocate, physician, and holistic trainer, I have seen the spectrum of varying degrees of achievement in some of the highest performers. I have worked with professional athletes, other physicians, professional musicians, professional stunt performers, and actors. I have worked with all walks of life from new-born infants to centenarians. I can tell you that there is one common denominator among us. The thing we all have in common is a desire to live. We all want to experience life— and as much of what life has to offer. The people I have seen that are the most successful and happiest are those that have adopted an "emotionally intelligent" perspective grounded in concepts of wellness. These performers are high achievers because they can confront reality as a dynamic thing that they have learned is influenced by their own thoughts and actions. They know that life is not just something that happens to them. They happen to life. They all share a commitment to being active participants in life, not just spectators.

Today, many high-profile, successful business people, are making their own wellness a priority and sharing their strategies with others. I've noticed recently how some of the high-profile success gurus have jumped on the health and wellness bandwagon and have written how-to books and articles and offered platforms for self-health improvement to the masses. Some of the more notable names are Tony Robbins, Grant Cardone, and Dean Graziosi to name a few. These men are all famous success-coaches, massively successful in business and in life themselves. They work on their own health and wellness and maintain great relationships with their families and help millions of people around the globe reach their own goals in life and business. But recently, they've all adopted a health-first mentality, recognizing the importance of prioritizing health to be our best.

Have you ever noticed the frequency of occurrences of famous and successful people who lose their lives early on due to some kind of tragedy? Usually, it's because of an addiction to drugs or alcohol. Sometimes there are just accidents, but it always reminds me of how our health and mortality trumps all other ways of accessing one's success or ability to enjoy life. Over the years, we've seen many music legends pass away too soon as they succumbed to the wrath of drugs. As Steve Jobs, the inventor of the iPhone was nearing the end of his life from the ravages of cancer, he said he would gladly give up everything for more time and life here with loved ones...

"At this moment, lying on the bed, sick and remembering all my life, I realize that all my recognition and wealth that I have is

meaningless in the face of imminent death," it goes on to say. "You can hire someone to drive a car for you, make money for you—but you cannot rent someone to carry the disease for you. One can find material things, but there is one thing that cannot be found when it is lost—life."

During her eulogy of her brother, Steve Jobs' sister, Mona Simpson, recounted Steve's final words as he had looked at those he loved around him and then beyond their faces when he said, "Oh wow... oh wow... oh wow." Perhaps he was able to see beyond and into the next life. He certainly was able to see ahead into the future in this life. But even with the great imagination and vision he had, Steve Jobs ultimately was forced to reconcile with the Blind Spot. Somewhere, somehow, along the incredible odyssey of his life and successes, he was unable to see where the interferences were to his health or where the contradictions may have been that steered his health into the direction of dis-ease.

We are living in a time when information is saturating our senses. We have instant access to as much knowledge as we want. And as I have stated earlier, the knowledge we accept as true and integrate into our consciousness, will either help guide us closer to the life we want, or will draw us further away. So, now the challenge is to filter the information and accept new data based upon not only empirical evidence, but also in considering how we will use it for our own good and for the good of those we have relationships with. An example of this is the dominance of social media today in purveying news, education, and entertainment to all of us. We can be selective in what we choose to view and decide what messaging we allow into our daily lives. But even more than this process of selection is coming to the realization that we can use this platform of social media to make a difference in the world. We can use it, rather than letting it use us! It is about making the decision to implement and gather information to use—not just to view it or think about it endlessly as a life-long spectator—but to use it to make ourselves better. Ultimately, it really comes down to discernment and application.

Along the way, as we learn some of these life-lessons, we can make changes that bring us more in line with the vision of success we have had for ourselves. We have discussed how contradictions in our individual philosophies can derail us.

If we can identify where the contradictions are and replace them with new philosophical premises, we go from frustration, disorganization, inefficiency, and even failure, to a place of confidence, organization, efficiency, and success.

Hopefully, along the journey of making these observations and necessary changes, we begin to see more clearly than ever and ultimately begin removing the obstacles we have placed in our own way.

Recognizing that we must re-define what success really means to us will speed the process up if we know where our contradictions are and we are able to make the appropriate replacements. This is more than likely going to be a life-long practice for most of us as we are all different and our health-needs are different. Discovering how to identify what is right for us takes time and a lot of attention. It is for this reason that the time to pay attention is now—before you lose your health. Success in any endeavor will be achieved by being aware and by remaining at peace with the notion that success is not a destination but an evolving, dynamic state of acceptance and evolution.

When we finally reach our goals, we often end up finding we are not necessarily fulfilled. Fulfillment is different than happiness. Fulfillment is more likely to occur when we are successful in living out our lives day to day with behaviors congruent with our philosophical premises. Once we achieve this degree of balance, we know we are living closer to our sense of purpose, and fulfillment becomes the natural consequence. I rarely find people that are truly fulfilled in their lives who are not healthy. They have succeeded in living a life that is constructive on all levels and avoided the destructive habits that would diminish their health, happiness, fulfillment, and ultimately, their potential as human beings.

As you consider the above ideas and the examples of others who had attained great financial wealth at the expense of their own health, do you feel any different about your own priorities?

Can you imagine the shift in your life happening as you become more focused on your health?

> ACTION STEP: Begin journaling your daily activities and weigh the difference between your constructive survival values vs. your destructive survival values. Look at how much time, energy and money you commit to each different category. You will quickly see where your focus and energy has been. Once you see your "health-balance sheet" in writing you'll be able to see where corrections need to occur.

THE RICHEST MAN IN THE HOSPITAL

CHAPTER 7

HEALTH IS YOUR GREATEST ASSET

By now, you have hopefully done some self-checking to figure out where you stand when it comes to your approach to achieving your goals and dreams and even how you live your life in general. Hopefully you've asked yourself where your own healthcare has been prioritized. I can tell you that in my own life, once I realized I would accelerate into greater achievement by refocusing my priorities and keeping them aligned with my overall philosophy of living a life in health and abundance, everything just got better. Had I not made the connection between removing those contradictions and being able to reach higher levels of success, I may not have grown to the level I have as a physician, husband, and father. I can say with complete resolve, that the moment my neighbor asked me the question about being the *Richest Man in the Hospital*, was the turning point for me. Even though I was not ready to fully live out the steps necessary for change, I did recognize the importance of his question and I knew sooner or later I would have to pay attention. You can only deny those kinds of lessons for so long before the universe makes you wake up and you don't want to wait for the awakening to happen while lying in a hospital bed!

It didn't take long for me to experience just what my neighbor had warned me of. I quickly made an "about-face" in my own health practices and set myself and my family, and my patients, on a course to get well and stay well. I can say with confidence, by applying the right philosophical premises to my understanding of what health was and applying the right actions, I have been able to remain well for decades since that incident. I have lived what it is like to not get sick and not have to miss out on a single day of work or anything to do with spending time with my family and friends. The lesson is simple, live with a focus toward building health not just mitigating symptoms.

After having watched so many friends and family members succumb to sickness and lose their lives, I began to see the true carnage in our society of sick, suffering, and dying people. I began to think of how rare it was to ever see an obese person when I was a kid—whether living out in the rural areas of the state or in the city we eventually moved to. As an adult, especially now, I see the incredible rise in sickness and disease to the point where now it's considered some kind of prejudice or elitism to desire being fit or to shop for whole-foods and take vitamins and other supplements. Although there is a growing awareness about health, nutrition, and exercise, there is at the very same time, a growing population of sick, obese, and chronically ill people. And there is a growing number of people suffering from mental illness and an explosion of available drugs ready to be pushed by Big Pharma and those who prescribe them. Seventy percent of U.S. adults are taking at least one prescription drug, and as a nation, consume the majority of drugs produced, despite having only five percent of the world population. And we are only becoming more and more sick.

I make mention of the "dying segment" in the sense that these people are existing on a plane of either ignorance, despair or possibly both. They may even just be apathetic. I am referring to the segment of the population in this country that has chosen to remain in a consciousness of denial and entranced by an assault of drug ads on TV re-minding them that they can continue living in dis-ease as long as they just take another pill. One of the more recent ads I've seen was one for diabetes drug (type 2— also known as lifestyle caused) lowering A-1C to control or manage diabetes all while watching a jubilant young, obese woman dancing and singing and running around. I can't help but see the irony in these ads. Why is she 100 pounds overweight if she's so active? And wouldn't it make more sense to correct the causes of her obesity than to learn how to live with it? (Diabetes and obesity often end up hand-in-hand). The real irony is that these days, one does not even need to leave the house to research anything they are interested in. All the information you could possibly need to help yourself and improve your life is right at your fingertips. All the resources you need for thriving are given to you by God. You just need to embrace them and implement. But the illness prevents it for so many as their depression or anxiety becomes the focus to treat with drugs rather than finding the true cause and focusing on ways to address them. These are illnesses that I see encouraged by the drug companies and catered to by our agencies. There are certainly some people who have legitimate mental health issues that require attention on some level. But I am talking about those who actively choose to check out on their own health, lives, and potential and their responsibilities to themselves and their families and even to their communities. They've either forgotten, never known or have been convinced they are not enough, don't have enough or aren't worthy of having the life and health of their dreams. The more I've studied the human body over my career, the more I'm convinced that we all have an incredible intelligence within us to maintain function and health in our bodies. And it reminds me of how when a baby is born everyone is so quick to exclaim "the miracle" of a new life coming into the world. I wonder, where do people think the miracle goes after birth? Does it just disappear? I tell people, when I do speak about what life and health are, "The miracle is still inside of you… you're just a bigger baby!"

Corinthians 3:16-17 asks us, "Don't you know that you yourselves are God's temple and that God's Spirit lives in you? "

It reminds me of Dr. B.J. Palmer's (the developer of chiropractic) prophetic statement, "If people got the 'Big Idea' (of chiropractic), the jails would be empty and the churches would be filled." He knew if people were educated to understand the great design of their bodies and their ability to heal and regulate through a healthy spine and nerve system, they could avoid the blind spots that ultimately cause disease. Today, we see the exact opposite as people are losing confidence in their own being. People aren't aware that health is the normal state and that one must be sick, to get sick. Many have abandoned their faith and desire for autonomy and self-responsibility and become the prey of government and institutions that facilitate dependency and abdicate responsibility for one's success, health, and happiness.

If we are going to succeed in life, we must see reality for what it is, not what we are told it is or what we would like to pretend it is. Ignoring causes (wrong diet, lack of exercise, poor attitude, toxic lifestyle, etc.) and living in denial will only guarantee a focus on treating effects. We must see where the contradictions are and take massive action, often in the complete opposite direction, to create the life we want.

We all know of people who have made great achievements in their respective fields only to lose everything because of the blind-spots or contradictions in their life-philosophies. Marriages fall apart, jobs are lost, bankruptcies are filed, and lives are lost. We've all seen the stories of famous celebrities—actors, athletes, musicians—all catapulted to ultra-fame and adored by millions, only to end up destroying their own lives with addictive behaviors of drug use, alcohol abuse, sex addiction or even food addiction. Somehow, for varying reasons no doubt, these people have fallen off track and their own challenges with contradictions in their lives became the dominant influence.

Sometimes the blind-spots that derail us are quite insidious. They come in many hidden forms on food labels, clothing labels, and messaging on TV and throughout the media that allow for new, destructive norms to sweep over an entire population. The unwitting consumer devours the lies and only very slowly begins the decline that keeps them losing instead of winning. It will require you, the consumer, to be more aware and to accept full responsibility for your own life and health. If you do accept responsibility for your life, achievement, and health, you will begin to thrive as you notice how much more energy you have and how much sharper your focus becomes. The most important step is adopting the approach that you alone must harness your thoughts and energy into a line of drive without contradictions, that will form an unstoppable energy and synergy for success. Once you have clarity on this, you will know you have made your claim to stand for a set of values that allows you to make great achievements in business, in relationships, and ultimately, your life.

In the end, your level of success in any area of your life will depend upon your abilities on many levels. You will make many decisions—some better than others. You will have successes and failures along the way. You may even lose everything only to learn from errors and come back stronger. But hopefully, after reading this, you will come to realize and then prioritize, that your health, and your faith above all else, will be the vehicles you will depend on for your success. Your health will allow you to overcome most obstacles if you protect it. If you do not, you will then know how costly that decision can be.

When you keep your health in focus and in first place, you have made the conscious decision that your health is your greatest asset. You can then go on to learn the how in getting, maintaining, and even multiplying your health-outcomes. The day you recognize that your health must be your number one priority is the day you begin to shrink the size of your Blind-Spot. As you move in that direction, you will begin to accumulate true wealth and abundant health—everything in life becomes more possible.

"How much better to seek wisdom than gold,
to get insight rather than silver"
—Proverbs

You will go on to a life of sustainable success and come closer to achieving all of your dreams as you move into the version of your best-self and your full potential.

Most of all, as you embrace this philosophy you will begin to see more clearly where the pitfalls are—where those contradictions are that detract you from being your best. As you will see, paying the Blind-Spot its due will keep you from becoming *The Richest Man in the Hospital.*

Ask yourself, "Can I truly see that I need to be healthy to fulfill my destiny?" "Do I do things on a daily basis to bring me closer to my health-potential?" "Are there obvious imbalances in my life that are bringing me closer to symptoms, sickness and disease?"

What would be the one thing you could do better today to start living a life of abundant health?

> ACTION STEP: Decide what that one thing could be and start implementing different behavior in that area today. By doing this you will make living a healthy lifestyle real to yourself and gain the con-

fidence from better self-control to go to your next level.

Keep the Picasso Principle alive in your mind and be patient but persistent in creating your new "health-compass" as you navigate your way to true success—your potential.

THE RICHEST MAN IN THE HOSPITAL

CHAPTER 8

REFLECTIONS

As I reflect back on when I first began to write this book I can see how critical it was for me to learn the above lessons and apply them to my life. I hope you see enough value in this to consider applying these ideas to your own life-strategy.

Today, at almost 56 years of age, I can tell you that by adopting a new approach without contradictions to my own life and health strategy, I've been able to remain well and very fit for the last twenty years. And besides the time period of getting off-track I had described; I haven't been sick in my adult life. The faith that God gave me all I need and all I must do is be a better steward of those gifts has led me to all the successes I had hoped for and a lot of that is because I've been able to remain super-healthy. Being with my wife for almost thirty years and raising super-healthy kids are among those incredible gifts. We have been able to serve and guide thousands of patients to greater health and lives over these years. I know that by subscribing to the tenets and philosophical guide in this book you can achieve all the success in life you want and keep your health in first-place at the same time!

A SUMMARY OF KEY POINTS
FOR EACH CHAPTER

CHAPTER 1 – *Introduction*

- The book aims to share insights about pursuing success in life and my personal story of that pursuit.
- It asks what success really means: is it money, status, material things? Or something else?
- The book will reveal a different truth about achieving lasting success and fulfillment.

CHAPTER 2 – *Thinking Back to Move Ahead*

- A past health scare made me realize I had neglected me health in pursuit of success.
- I recalled my neighbor's warning about being "the richest man in the hospital."
- The incident forced me to re-examine my priorities and focus more on my health.

CHAPTER 3 – *Nobody is Coming to Rescue You*

- I realized I had to take responsibility for improving my own health.
- I researched how to build a strong immune system and live a healthy lifestyle.
- I saw contradictions between healthcare system/government guidelines and true health.

CHAPTER 4 – *The Potential Power of Knowledge*

- Knowledge is only powerful if we apply it through strategies and action.
- We can be trapped by "cognitive dissonance," unable to accept new information that contradicts our beliefs.
- I aim to provide knowledge to help people get healthier.

CHAPTER 5 – *Taking the Risk of Being Healthy*

- Making real changes to improve health requires risk and discomfort.
- Fear of standing out from others prevents change.
- We must forego "fitting in" and be willing to pursue health even if others don't understand.

CHAPTER 6 – *The Picasso Principle*

- Excellence requires lifelong diligence and practice, not just occasional effort.
- Like Picasso's art, a lifetime of work made his final paintings seem effortless.
- Creating health takes daily focus over years, not quick fixes.

CHAPTER 7 – *Re-defining Success*

- Success defined by money/fame alone often leads to unhappiness and poor health.
- True success combines achievement and excellent health/relationships.
- We must identify and eliminate contradictions between our beliefs and actions.

CHAPTER 8 – *Health is Your Greatest Asset*

- Making health the top priority is key to sustainable success.
- Ignoring health and indulging in "average" norms leads to decline.
- We have incredible self-healing ability if we remove interferences and live congruently.

ABOUT THE AUTHOR

D r. Chris Condon, D.C. is a practicing chiropractic physician currently directing clinic operations in Scottsdale, Arizona. Following graduation from Fitchburg State University in Massachusetts, he went on to earn his doctorate degree at Life University in Marietta, Georgia. While a student at Life, he led the prestigious University's school newspaper as the Editor-in-Chief and self-published two books as guides for overall clinical excellence, patient education, and wellness strategies. During that time, he also became certified by the International Chiropractic Association as a Sports and Fitness Chiropractor and paired that knowledge with his decades of experience as a trainer and natural bodybuilder to guide patients in their wellness and fitness endeavors.

Following graduation, Dr. Condon opened his first clinic in Andover, Massachusetts and there built one of the most successful practices of its kind in the country. Within two years, he opened a second clinic specializing in injury rehabilitation. Having served hundreds of patients every week for over twenty years, and specializing in non-surgical spinal corrective care, Dr. Condon has continued to add to his areas of expertise as a specialist in non-surgical spinal decompression and the treatment of disc disorders and neuropathy as well as becoming a consultant for other doctors and medical device companies.

When not working he can be found in the gym, reading, or spending time with his family.

Made in USA - North Chelmsford, MA
41588_9781959608608
12.08.2023 0510